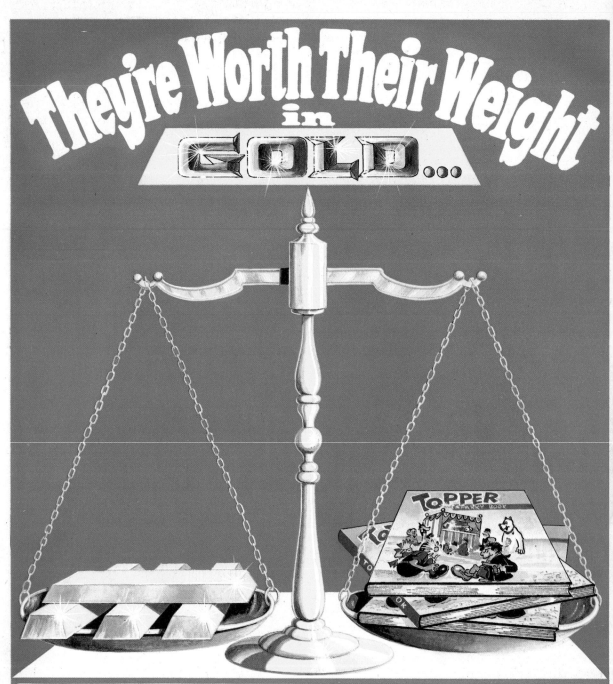

They're Worth Their Weight in **GOLD**...

..... *And this copy belongs to*

NAME Christopher Hunter
ADDRESS 23 Forest road Townhill Dunfermline Fife

SO, HANDS OFF!

Printed and Published by
D. C. THOMSON & CO., LTD.,
185, Fleet Street,
London EC4A 2HS.

IN THE WHOLE, WIDE WORLD, HE'S THE ONE AND ONLY THINGUMMYBLOB

PROFESSOR POTT CREATED HIM...

...AND NOW HE CAN'T STAND THE SIGHT OF HIM.

FIRE

Here you see one of the early methods of fire-fighting. The townsfolk—for there was no organised fire-fighting services until the 17th century—tore down the blazing buildings with long, hooked poles known as fire hooks. In this way, they hoped to prevent the fire from spreading to other buildings.

SUN FIREMAN

SUN FIRE-MARK

7313

3105

LONDON ASSURANCE FIRE-MARK

LONDON ASSURANCE FIREMAN

The first real fire-brigades were founded in the 17th and 18th centuries by insurance companies. Each company fire-brigade had its own particular uniform. A brigade would only tackle a fire in a building which was insured with its company. Such buildings always displayed the company's sign, or fire-mark, as it was called.

Fire-pumps of the 18th century needed up to twenty men to work the pump handles, and spectators watching a fire were often offered a shilling to man the pump. Sometimes there was such a rush to earn a shilling that a free fight broke out round the pump. Then the firemen had to fight the would-be helpers—and the fire!

The first steam-powered fire-pump was invented in 1829. It could pump water out at a rate of 170 gallons per minute and send a jet almost 100 feet high. By the middle of the century, horse-drawn engines with steam pumps were being used by many fire-brigades.

The first fire-engines were crude affairs. By operating the levers on this 17th century engine, water could be pumped from the barrel-shaped tank, but the tank had to be filled continuously from buckets.

Blazing chimneys were often the start of much bigger fires. One of the recognised ways of dealing with a chimney fire was to fire a gun up the chimney, dislodging the blazing soot so that it could be easily dealt with when it fell down to the hearth.

Often a company fire-brigade would turn up at a fire, only to discover that the blazing building was not insured by their company. Then the men of that brigade would stand by and jeer at their rival company's efforts to put out the fire! Eventually this practice ceased, and the brigades fought any fire, side by side.

This wheeled fire-escape was in use at the time of steam fire-engines. The main ladder was about 35 feet long, and attached to the underside of it was a canvas chute down which people could slide to safety. An extra ladder could be raised to windows above the chute.

This type of pump and fire escape was the first of its kind in Britain. It went into use in 1904. It was engine-driven, and the engine could also pump water through the hoses at the rate of 250 gallons a minute.

Here's a chum who'll tickle you—with a Christmas trick or two!

TRICKY DICKY

HEE! HEE! I'VE GOT A FEW TRICKY CHRISTMAS PRESENTS I'M GOING TO GIVE TO FOLK.

AH! THE THOMSON TWINS—I'VE GOT A PRESENT FOR THEM! GIGGLE!

HI, TWINS, WANT TO PULL A CHRISTMAS CRACKER?

GOSH! TA, DICKY!

OOH! IT'S STRETCHING!

THIS GAG'S A "CRACKER"!

HO! HO! THAT'S MY RUBBER CRACKER FOR PEOPLE WHO DON'T LIKE NOISE!

A gag that's hot as mustard—with Christmas pud and custard.

He gets in the way—of his own trickery!

ALi's BABA
THE BABE WITH THE INVISIBLE BODYGUARD

NICK KELLY
SPECIAL AGENT

AND **CEDRIC**

IN THE CASE OF THE

TROUBLESOME TREE!

TAKING THESE VALUABLE JEWELS TO THE STRONG BOX AT THE BANK FOR MR BINKS SHOULD BE A PIECE OF CAKE, CEDRIC.

J. BINKS JEWELLERS

'S FUNNY! I DON'T REMEMBER THAT TREE.

WHUMP!

THUNK!

OH, NO—A TREE BANDIT!

HEH-HEH!

COME ON, CEDRIC! LET'S GET AFTER THAT TREE!

LOOK—THERE IT IS. IT MUST HAVE STOPPED WHEN IT SAW THAT BOBBY.

QUICK, CONSTABLE! HELP US TO ARREST THIS TREE!

CHEEP! CHEEP!

CRACK!

AHEM! IT'S THE WRONG TREE, CEDRIC.

BIRDS'- NEST SNATCHERS, EH? C'MON DOWN TO THE STATION.

WE CAN EXPLAIN, CONSTABLE!

NEXT DAY, KELLY AND CEDRIC GET A SECURITY ESCORT JOB...

YOUR BAG OF MONEY WILL BE QUITE SAFE WHILE **WE'RE** AROUND, MR MUNNIEBAGS.

BANK

HMM! A TREE IN THE MIDDLE OF THE PATH? THAT'S SUSPICIOUS.

A brief-case brief chase!

A helping hand from a busy beak!

Ever so naughty—but always good for a laugh! That's . . .

She's acting the fool—as Beryl, the bull!

There's a reason behind—her daft games, you'll soon find.

Baron von Reichs-Pudding

Things don't go as planned over No Man's Land!

Direct hits by der Pong-blitz!

THE ONE AND ONLY BUFFALO BILL

WILLIAM FREDERICK CODY, or Buffalo Bill, as he is better known, is probably the most famous of all the heroes of the Wild West. During his exciting lifetime, he was a soldier, scout, Indian fighter, buffalo hunter and showman, and many stirring tales are told of his amazing adventures.

Buffalo Bill spent part of his boyhood in Fort Levenworth, in Kansas, where his father owned the general store. Many Indians from nearby reservations came to trade at the store, and from the Indian boys young Bill Cody learned the Indian language and how to shoot with bow and arrows.

Buffalo Bill won his famous nickname because of his prowess at hunting the bison, or "buffaloes" as they were called, which roamed the prairie in huge herds at that time. When the Kansas Pacific Railroad was being built, Bill was engaged as a buffalo hunter. He had to supply fresh buffalo meat to the gangs of workmen laying the tracks. Once, in a contest with another hunter called Bill Comstock, Bill shot 69 buffaloes to Comstock's 46. Because of this feat, Buffalo Bill was named the champion buffalo hunter of the plains.

Buffalo Bill formed a circus—the Wild West Show—which toured America and Europe for many years with great success. It featured rifle and revolver shooting, and there were many crackshots in the show. One of them was a woman, the famous Annie Oakley, shown here with Buffalo Bill shooting coloured glass balls tossed into the air.

Before he was twelve years old, Bill Cody was working as a waggon-train messenger. His job was to keep contact between two columns of waggons, about fifteen miles apart, which were carrying supplies to frontier posts. On one occasion, he and two companions were ambushed by Indians. The three formed their mules into a triangular barricade, and from behind it they opened fire on the Indians and drove them off.

While still in his teens, Buffalo Bill went gold prospecting in the Pike's Peak district of Colorado. When returning home downriver the raft on which he and his companions were travelling capsized in dangerous rapids. Luckily, all the men managed to swim to safety.

At one time, Bill Cody was a Pony Express rider. These riders, on very fast horses, carried mail and messages between frontier settlements. It was dangerous work, as the riders were often attacked by bandits or hostile Indians.

The most exciting part of the Wild West Show was when a stagecoach, driven by Buffalo Bill and drawn by six galloping horses, charged into the arena. Suddenly, the coach was attacked by a band of howling, whooping Indians in full war-dress. The gallant passengers in the coach opened fire on the Indians. Of course, blank cartridges were used, but the effect was very realistic and the audience were thrilled to see the marksmen picking off the Indians one by one, and the coach making its escape from the ambush.

HUNGRY HORACE

Dear Santa

Is it an elephant? Is it a mountain? No—it's . . .

Tiny
THE WORLD'S BIGGEST DOG!

Is he REALLY below—that great mountain of snow?

THE WONDERFUL WHIZZERS from OZZ

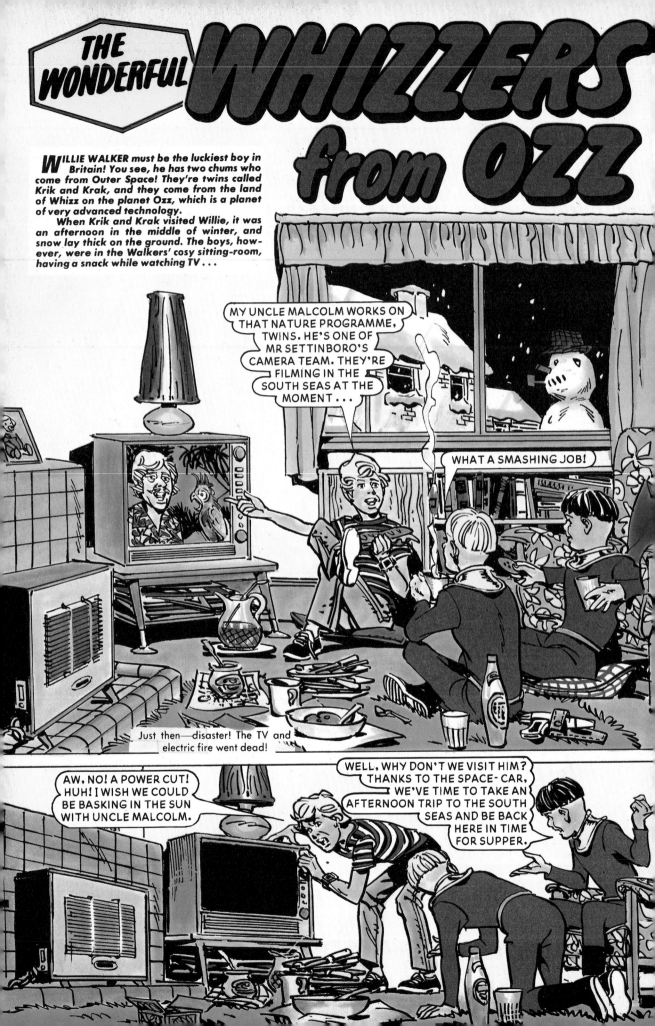

WILLIE WALKER must be the luckiest boy in Britain! You see, he has two chums who come from Outer Space! They're twins called Krik and Krak, and they come from the land of **Whizz** on the planet **Ozz**, which is a planet of very advanced technology.

When Krik and Krak visited Willie, it was an afternoon in the middle of winter, and snow lay thick on the ground. The boys, however, were in the Walkers' cosy sitting-room, having a snack while watching TV . . .

MY UNCLE MALCOLM WORKS ON THAT NATURE PROGRAMME, TWINS. HE'S ONE OF MR SETTINBORO'S CAMERA TEAM. THEY'RE FILMING IN THE SOUTH SEAS AT THE MOMENT . . .

WHAT A SMASHING JOB!

Just then—disaster! The TV and electric fire went dead!

AW, NO! A POWER CUT! HUH! I WISH WE COULD BE BASKING IN THE SUN WITH UNCLE MALCOLM.

WELL, WHY DON'T WE VISIT HIM? THANKS TO THE SPACE-CAR, WE'VE TIME TO TAKE AN AFTERNOON TRIP TO THE SOUTH SEAS AND BE BACK HERE IN TIME FOR SUPPER.

So, armed with towels and trunks, the Whizzer Twins and Willie rushed out to the Twins' marvellous space-car, which sat in the garden.

Within seconds, the amazing Whizz-car had shot out into Space, and was soon curving back to Earth towards the South Seas.

WE'RE RIGHT ON COURSE FOR THE AREA WHERE YOUR UNCLE IS. IT SHOULD BE EARLY MORNING THERE.

Far below, a Jumbo-jet was streaking through the clouds.

On board, terror gripped the passengers. A gang of hijackers—posing as ordinary tourists—had just made their bid to take over the plane.

LISTEN HERE, AN' LISTEN GOOD—IF THIS PILOT DON'T TAKE US TO WHERE WE WANNA GO, I TAKE MY THUMB OFF THE PIN OF THIS GRENADE HERE ... AN' BOOM—IT'LL BE CURTAINS FOR ALL OF US!

Suddenly, without warning, a panicking traveller lashed out with his arm, knocking the live grenade from the hijacker's hand!

AAH!

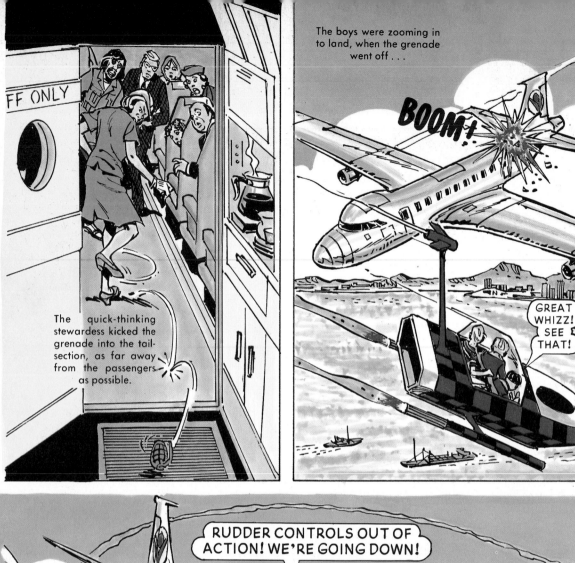

FF ONLY

The quick-thinking stewardess kicked the grenade into the tail-section, as far away from the passengers as possible.

The boys were zooming in to land, when the grenade went off . . .

BOOM!

GREAT WHIZZ! SEE THAT!

RUDDER CONTROLS OUT OF ACTION! WE'RE GOING DOWN!

The jet-liner was set in a screaming crash-dive for the sea. Krik swerved the space-car round so that it was just below the stricken aircraft. At the same moment, Krak jabbed a button on the controls, and a shimmering ray shone from the base of the Whizz-car. Almost instantly the surface of the sea became a solid block of ice!

LET'S HOPE THE FREEZO-RAY CAN MAKE A WIDE ENOUGH STRIP FOR THE PLANE TO LAND ON.

Krik brought the space-car swooping in silently to hover close by the plane's control cabin. One of the hijackers was holding a gun to the pilot's head.

OKAY, BUSTER...SHOW US WHERE YOUR LIFE-SAVING EQUIPMENT IS ...AND FAST!

Now Krak took swift aim with his amazing Ozz-pistol. Then he fired! The hijackers were slammed across the cabin as if socked by a heavy-weight boxer!

Meanwhile, in the glare of the scorching sun, the ice-patch supporting the Jumbo-jet already showed signs of breaking up. The great plane began to sink, until another ray from the back of the space-car seemed to grab the plane as if in an invisible hand.

MAGNETO-RAY IN ACTION. PREPARE FOR FULL-POWER THRUST.

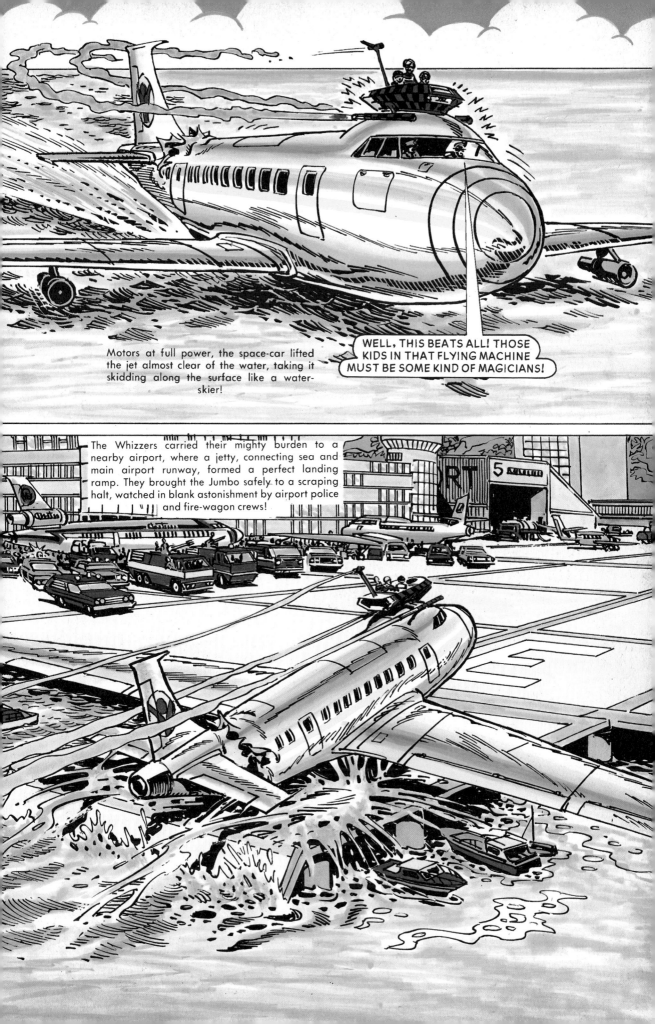

Motors at full power, the space-car lifted the jet almost clear of the water, taking it skidding along the surface like a water-skier!

WELL, THIS BEATS ALL! THOSE KIDS IN THAT FLYING MACHINE MUST BE SOME KIND OF MAGICIANS!

The Whizzers carried their mighty burden to a nearby airport, where a jetty, connecting sea and main airport runway, formed a perfect landing ramp. They brought the Jumbo safely to a scraping halt, watched in blank astonishment by airport police and fire-wagon crews!

With the jet safely in the hands of the emergency services, Willie, Krik and Krak shut off the magneto-ray and prepared to take off again.

THEY'LL BE SAFE NOW. COME ON, TWINS. IT'S TIME WE SET OFF TO SEE UNCLE MALCOLM.

Suddenly—

OH, CRIKEY! THE TAIL SECTION'S BREAKING AWAY. IT'LL CRASH DOWN ON THOSE POLICEMEN! DO SOMETHING, KRIK!

Krik moved like lightning. Slamming down a switch, he sent a blast of compressed air hissing from a nozzle on the front of the space-car, and hit the tail-section square-on.

It's IMPossible not to laugh at ...

SPLODGE

THE LAST OF THE GOBLINS

BAH! IT'S BEEN POURING RAIN FOR DAYS! I'M JUST ABOUT SICK OF IT.

US TOO!

IT'S NO BETTER INSIDE—THE RAIN HAS SOAKED RIGHT THROUGH.

HEY! I'VE AN IDEA!

I AM LEAVING THE FOREST, MY FRIENDS, TO LIVE IN A DRY, RAINPROOF PLACE. FAREWELL.

EH?

YOU'RE JOKING!

WHERE?

ANY ROOM FOR US?

HEY—WAIT FOR US, SPLODGE!

BUZZ OFF—AN' THINK UP YOUR OWN BRIGHT IDEAS!

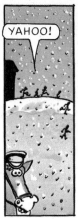

Paint of all hues gives Mickey the blues!

ALL ABOARD

HOW ANIMALS CARRY THEIR YOUNG

When the American Opossum moves her family from one place to another, she curves her tail over her back. The young opossums hook their own tails round their mother's and hold tight while she carries them along.

Here you see a young kangaroo in his mother's pouch. Even when he is old enough to move about on his own, he will return to the pouch if danger threatens.

This South American Ant-eater is carrying her young one on her back.

When a Polar Bear goes for a swim, her cub hangs on to her tail and gets a tow.

The Koala Bear of Australia is a lovely little animal. The Koala cub is carried everywhere on his mother's back until he has grown almost as big as she is.

The Flying Squirrel glides from branch to branch with her young firmly gripped in her mouth.

Although a young Hippopotamus is able to swim when only a few hours old, he is not sufficiently speedy to keep up with his mother. So when she swims fast he rides on her back.

Here you see how the Sloth of South and Central America, which spends most of its time hanging upside down, carries its young.

A Lioness carries her cubs by the scruff of their necks, just as cats carry their kittens.

BAH! I CAN'T SEE AGAIN, NOW THAT THE RAY'S WORN OFF.

AHEM! WATCH CAREFULLY AND BEFORE YOUR VERY EYES . . .

. . . THE PILE OF SCARVES GROWS AND GROWS.

HEH! HEH! I KNOW WHAT— I'LL GROW MY HEAD A BIT!

LW SW

THAT'S BETTER!

ERK!

HEY! I DON'T KNOW WHAT YOU'VE DONE, BUT NOW I CAN'T SEE.

SORRY! I'LL DO SOMETHING ABOUT IT.

GRR! HE'S RUINING MY PERFORMANCE!

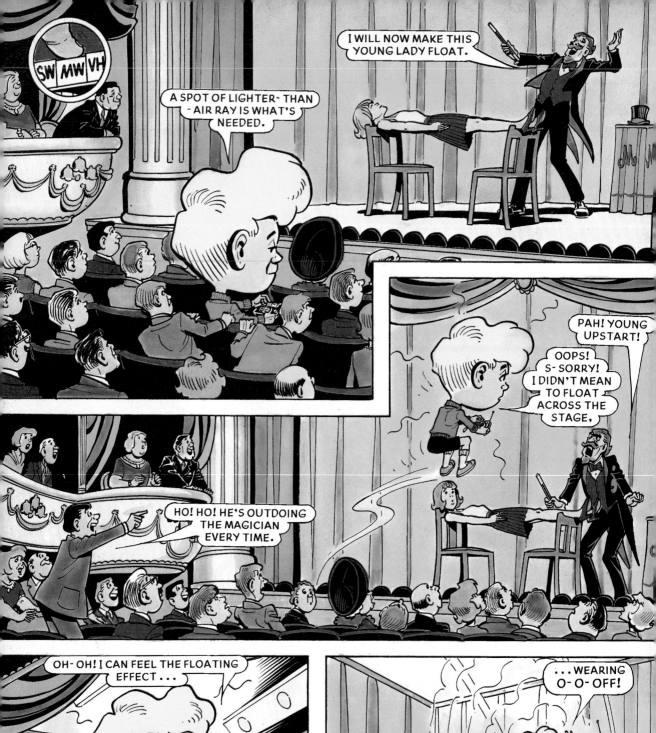

Trouble afoot—till Blow gives a toot!

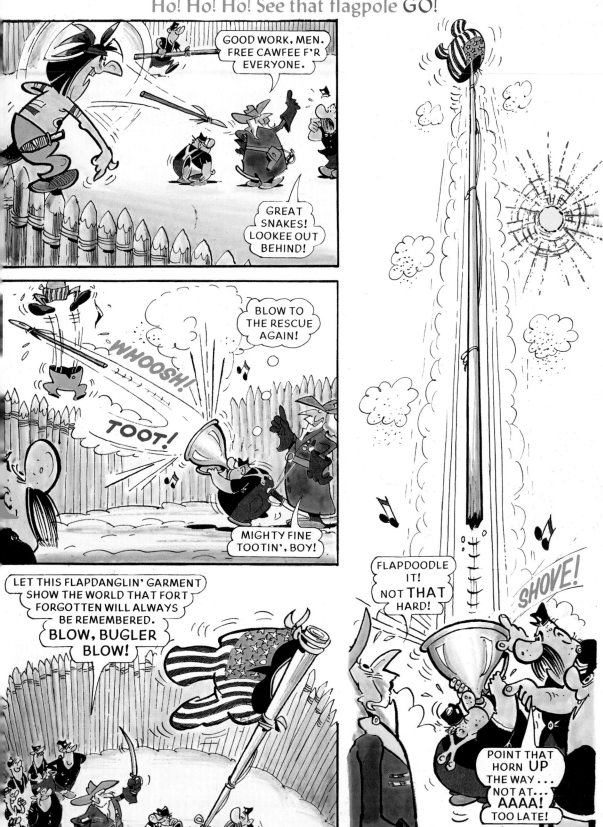

PETER PIPER

THERE'S NOTHING WRONG WITH HIM, MRS PIPER, EXCEPT A SLIGHT TUMMY UPSET. GET HIM UP. LYING IN BED ISN'T GOOD FOR HIM.

'BYE, FOLKS!

PAH! I'VE MISSED THE PERFORMANCE!

COMING TO THE TOWN HALL. BRITAIN'S No 1 POP STAR CHRIS O'BRIEN

I'LL TRY AGAIN!

OOH! THIS IS RIDICULOUS.

BILLY HEART'S CIRCUS

A CIRCUS. NOW THAT'S ALWAYS ENTERTAINING.

YOU'D BETTER GET BACK TO BED AT ONCE.

HMM! EH? WHAT? AT ONCE? OH, RIGHT, DOCTOR.

TOO DAZED TO THINK STRAIGHT

MARY QUAINT'S CONTINENTAL QUILTS

FOXY

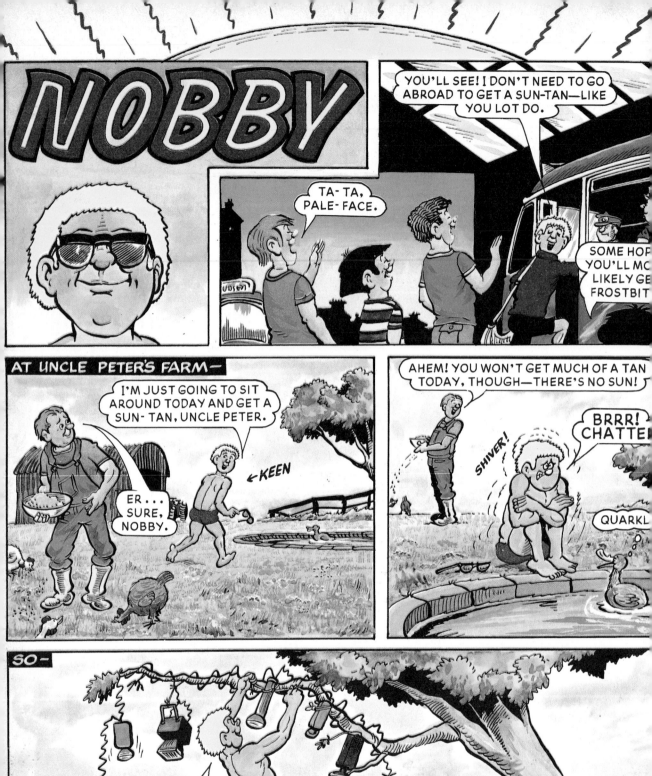

When he opens the door—he's a pale-face once more!

NOBBY'S KNOW-HOW
HOW TO MAKE A SUPER WHIRLER

1. You'll need a piece of paper about 9 inches square, a pencil, a ruler, scissors, a pin and a small stick.

2. Measure one inch in from each corner of the paper, as shown in the diagram, and make a small mark with your pencil. Join the marks on opposite sides with a pencil line. Then measure an inch out from the point where the lines meet, on each line, and make another small mark.

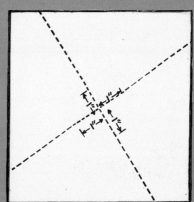

3. Next, cut down each line to the marks you made (or get your Mum or Dad to help if you're not allowed to use scissors.)

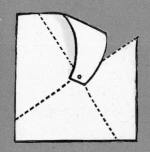 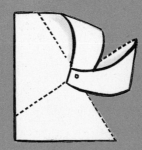

4. Now fold each corner into the centre, and stick a pin through all the thicknesses of paper, making sure the pin is centrally placed.

5. Now your super whirler is ready for use. If you like, you can make two, paint them different colours, and put them on the same pin or wire, separated by a bead.

Pin stuck through windmill and bead, into the stick.

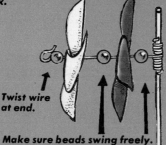

Twist wire at end.

Make sure beads swing freely.

WHIRRR

WULF OF THE ARROWS

THE Vikings of Harvik were preparing for a great voyage to the warm seas of the south—a voyage in search of trade and treasure.
Only a bowman was needed to complete the crew of their longship, the Drakkon, and so a keen archery contest was taking place. Young Wulf looked on with interest.

Suddenly, behind Wulf, a salmon leaped high out of the water. Quick as a flash, he snatched up his bow and arrow . . .

. . . and fired!

Wulf dived in after the stricken salmon.

DID YOU SEE THAT, VARDA?

NOW TO GET IT!

Carrying his prize, the sturdy young Viking splashed ashore. To his amazement, the two leaders of the Norsemen, Varda and Ironfist, offered him the final place in the picked crew of the Drakkon!

WHAT SAY YOU HE SAILS WITH US?

YES, VARDA! THE BOY HAS PROVED HIS SKILL.

The crew carried the delighted boy shoulder-high to the longship.

Later that day, the Drakkon set sail. The great voyage had begun.

Wulf and his comrades sailed ever southward, reaching, at length, seas where flying fish abounded. Buckets of cooling sea water refreshed the toiling oarsmen.

After many more days at sea the keen eyes of [V]arda spotted the welcome sight of land —the coast of North Africa!

LAND AHOY!

The Drakkon swept inshore towards a bay. Drawing closer, the Norsemen saw a Moorish township, previously hidden by a headland.

But this was a shore that welcomed no strangers. The longship's approach sent Moorish sentries scurrying into action.

HURRY! HURRY! YOU KNOW WHAT TO DO!

A mighty siege-engine—part of the township's defences —stood on the headland below which the Drakkon sailed. A large, liquid-filled bottle was hurriedly prepared as ammunition . . .

. . . and catapulted in a great downward arc towards the unsuspecting Vikings.

The flying bottle smashed, dead on target, on the deck of the longship.

Dense fumes of gas from the escaping liquid sent Vikings falling senseless on all sides.

BY THOR! WHAT STRANGE WEAPON IS THIS?

Once the gas had cleared, scores of Moors sailed out in small boats, and swarmed victoriously over the Drakkon.

THIS SHIP IS OURS, MY FRIENDS!

The Vikings' captors carried them ashore and took them straight to a sea-front prison.

Gradually the groggy Norsemen came to their senses. The first sounds that greeted them were the taunts of Moorish children, who had come to mock the prisoners.

YAH! GREAT HORNED GOATS!

Rotten fruit and even bamboo sticks were hurled through the prison bars.

LOOK OUT!

At last, tired of their cruel game, the young Moors moved away. Wulf looked out and, trembling with excitement, spotted Ironfist's great hammer, resting against a capstan.

OVER THERE! LOOK!

Wulf took an arrowhead from his pocket. He had a plan.

Having bound the arrowhead firmly to one of the bamboo rods thrown into the cell, Wulf used another rod to make a bow. Then he was ready!

With a length of twine tied to the arrow, Wulf drew the bowstring, aimed and fired at the shaft of the hammer.

The light arrow glanced off the rounded hammer shaft—but, by sheer luck, passed through the leather loop attached to it.

A Moorish guard stood unsuspecting as Wulf gently drew in the hammer by means of the twine attached to the arrow.

The hammer safely in his grasp, Ironfist lifted it into the cell. Then he prepared to attack the stout, iron-bound door.

NOW THEY WILL SEE HOW I GOT MY NAME OF IRONFIST!

With a mighty blow, the upper hinge was sent flying. A second blow carried the whole door crashing outwards.

COME QUICK! THE HORNED ONES ARE ESCAPING!

Jubilantly, the crew charged out into the African sunshine and raced down towards the quayside.

The shackled Vikings leaped aboard their vessel, and hastened to set sail.

But the Moors were speedily on the scene. Their leader carried one of the deadly bottles. And now . . .

Wulf's aim shattered the bottle in mid-air!

Another bottle was thrown, but again Wulf was ready and it, too, burst well short of the longship. The dense gas released by the bottles billowed back onto the quayside.

The Norsemen roared with laughter as their enemies dropped senseless, one by one. A solitary Moor avoided the choking fumes—but there was nothing he could do now to prevent the Vikings sailing safely seaward.

Once out at sea, Varda and Ironfist honoured the brave boy bowman.

HIGH

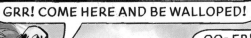

LOW

FROM CHARLIES TO BOBBIES

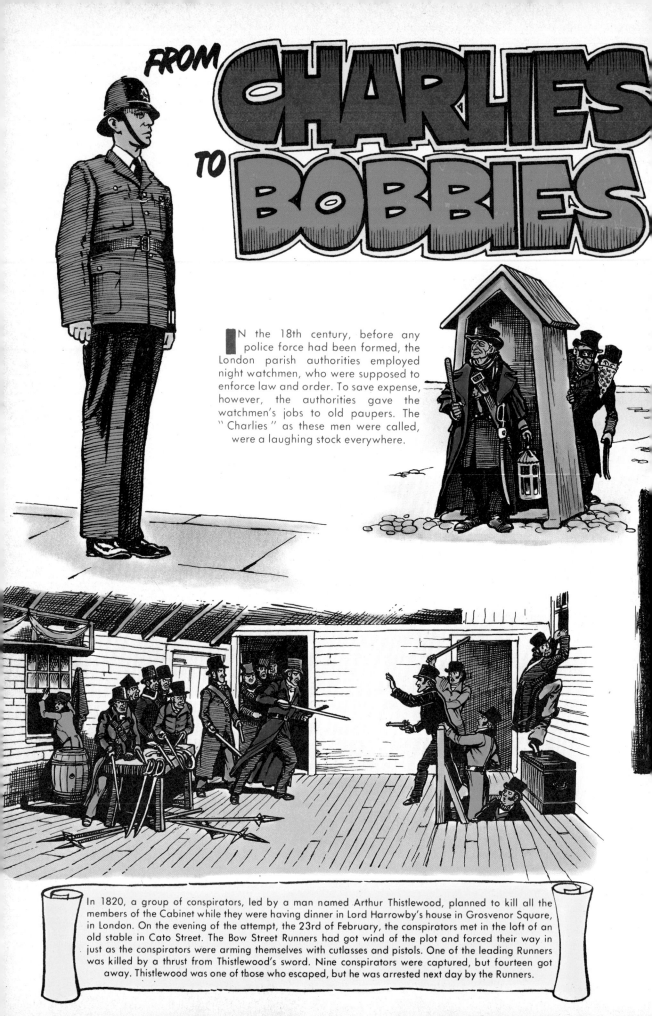

IN the 18th century, before any police force had been formed, the London parish authorities employed night watchmen, who were supposed to enforce law and order. To save expense, however, the authorities gave the watchmen's jobs to old paupers. The "Charlies" as these men were called, were a laughing stock everywhere.

In 1820, a group of conspirators, led by a man named Arthur Thistlewood, planned to kill all the members of the Cabinet while they were having dinner in Lord Harrowby's house in Grosvenor Square, in London. On the evening of the attempt, the 23rd of February, the conspirators met in the loft of an old stable in Cato Street. The Bow Street Runners had got wind of the plot and forced their way in just as the conspirators were arming themselves with cutlasses and pistols. One of the leading Runners was killed by a thrust from Thistlewood's sword. Nine conspirators were captured, but fourteen got away. Thistlewood was one of those who escaped, but he was arrested next day by the Runners.

sorts of tricks were
~~ed on the poor old
~~rlie. A favourite game
~~ to sneak up behind his
~~ry box, then overturn it
~~d pin him underneath.

During the second half of the 18th century, the Bow Street Runners were formed to fight against crime. Because they wore scarlet waistcoats, these men were known as " Robin Redbreasts "

The crowned baton badge of authority carried by the Runners.

" Double - Head " Townsend, most famous of the Bow Street Runners, was a great favourite with King George III and also with William IV. One of his duties was to attend Court functions to see that no jewellery was stolen.

The heaths and outlying districts of London were infested with highwaymen. To stamp out this menace, the Horse Patrol was formed in 1805. They were so successful that, before long, the activities of the highwaymen almost ceased.

At the beginning of the 19th century, Foot Patrols were raised to range the criminal areas of London. The men of the patrols, in constant danger of attack, worked in groups of five or six.

The greatest step in London's fight against crime came in 1829, when Sir Robert Peel founded the Metropolitan Police Force, The men of his force got the name of " Peelers " or " Bobbies ".

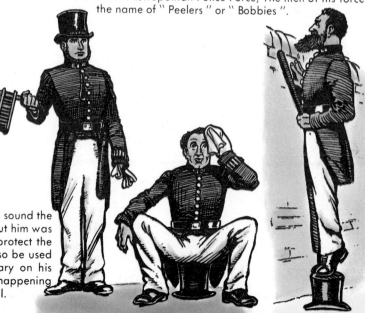

This early policeman carried a rattle to sound the alarm, but the most unusual thing about him was his top-hat. It was lined with steel to protect the wearer from cudgel-blows. It could also be used as a seat when the Peeler grew weary on his beat, or as a " step " to see what was happening on the other side of a high wall.

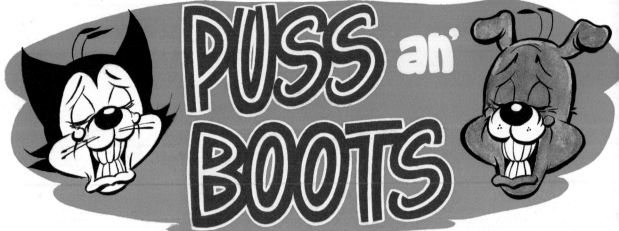

The famous, funny pair—who get in each other's hair!

PUSS an' BOOTS

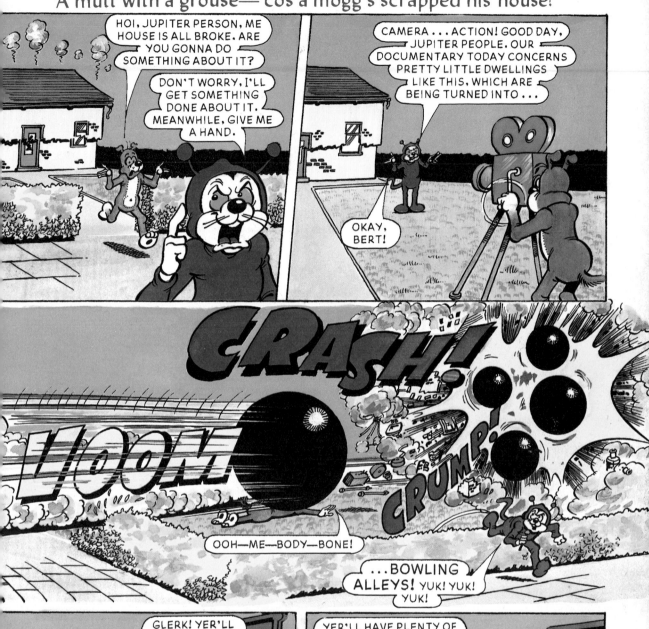

They didn't BEWARE OF THE PERIL!

THAT DOES IT, MY GIRL! NO MORE BIKES FOR YOU! YOU'RE A DANGER ON THE ROAD!

AW, DAD! I JUST BENT IT A TEENSY BIT!

LATER—

HERE'S WHAT I NEED—MY OLD SCOOTER.

BUT THIS IS NO FUN...UNLESS...

...I PUT A BIT OF SPEED ON! YAHOO!

A very odd parking spot—that doesn't suit Kelly a lot!

Ding! Dong! Dell! Guess who's in a bell?

Rocket-powered shocks—and a pond full of crocs!

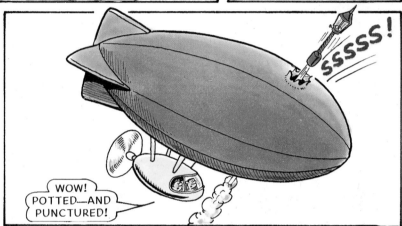

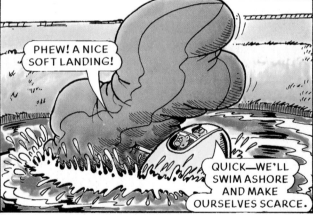

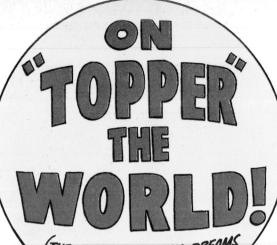

ON "TOPPER" THE WORLD!

(THE FAVOURITE DAY-DREAMS OF FAMOUS FUN FOLK!)

What a happy day for Beryl—a slipper bonfire on Guy Fawkes night!

The school sports is just a "walk-over" when Danny Wilson is day-dreaming!

Dicky's great dream is of helping Dad about the house...

Tiny would love to help in an archaeological "dig"

PULL!

WHAT DO YOU MEAN, "GIVE ME THIS BONE I FOUND?" I WOULDN'T DREAM OF IT!

TUT! I MUST HAVE LEFT THE DOOR OPEN!

SLAM!

POLICE

Fred day-dreams of finding unlocked doors...

...and never of finding locked ones!

JIMMY JINX AND WHAT HE THINKS

YOU SHOULD PLAY FOOTBALL IN THE PARK.

THE PARK'S MILES AWAY, JIM—PLAY HERE.

I'VE INVITED MY PALS ROUND TO PLAY FOOTBALL. I'LL WORK OUT A PITCH.

AW, STOP ARGUING. I'M PLAYING HERE!

YES, THIS'LL MAKE A GOOD GOAL POST!

WOW! SORRY AGAIN, DAD!

ERK!

PLEASE TAKE MY ADVICE, JAMES...

DON'T SAY A WORD. I'M LOOKING FOWARD TO A GOOD GAME OF FOOTBALL.

WE'LL HAVE TO KICK OFF FROM THE MIDDLE OF THIS FLOWER BED.

MY FLOWERS!